Prolance

www.prolancewriting.com
California, USA
©2018 Alia G. Dada
Illustrations ©2018 Robin Boyer

ISBN: 978-0-9996991-1-9

Bedtime
Sunnahs

Emulating the Prophet one night at a time

Written by Alia G. Dada
Illustrated by Robin Boyer

PROLANCE

◄ • Dedication • ►

In the Name of God, the Most
Gracious the Most Merciful.
Nothing is possible without Him,
and our reward is with Him.

To all the mothers, fathers, and
caregivers struggling to raise God
fearing children.

To my family and husband who have
always supported me.

To my children who constantly
inspire me.

This is for you.

It's time to go night night.

We brush our teeth,

we make wudu,

pj's on, you know what to do.

We hop into bed,
read a book or two,
it's time to sleep.

No wait, we have some Sunnahs to keep!

Praising Allah puts light in our heart so that it shines.

We say our Athkar,
Al Humdulillah 33 times,
SubhanAllah 33 times, and
Allahu Akbar 34 times.

Don't forget the 3 Quls,
the last 3 chapters of The Quran.
We recite them every day, morning and night,
to keep all the bad things away.

Hands up, hands up, we must make dua before we close our eyes.
Let's raise our hands up towards the skies.

Ask Allah for all that you dream, but don't forget the people you love, the sick, the needy and the entire Ummah...

Ameen!

We say Bismillah before we lay down our head,
hugs and kisses for our loved ones.

We turn towards the right as our Prophet
(Sallalahu Alayhi Wa Salam) said,
then we doze off to bed.

◄ • Appendix • ►

Parents Notes

When it comes to children, our priority should be fostering a love of Allah, His messenger and His deen. The purpose of this book is for children to learn and memorize the Sunnahs before going to bed in a positive way, through its nightly reading.

In the hopes of increasing Islamic literacy amongst the children of our Ummah I have listed all the accompanying ahadeeth for your children's reference as well as additional bedtime Sunnahs for those more advanced. And a fun activity to help increase Islamic literacy would be for them to look up the hadith themselves .

◄ • Appendix • ►
Islamic Terminology

1. Allah: God, the One and Only

2. Sunnah: The way of the Prophet Muhammad (peace be upon him) embodied in the things he said, did, and through his noble character.

3. Al Humdulillah: All praise is for Allah

4. SubhanAllah: How perfect Allah is

5. Allahu Akbar: Allah is Greater than all things

6. MashAllah: Allah has willed/allowed something to happen; expressed to show joy, and happiness

7. Dua: Asking Allah what is beneficial for us (and others), and asking Allah to remove what is harmful for us (and others). It is asking Allah for help and support.

8. Ummah: The entire Muslim population around the world

9. Bismillah: In the name of God

10. Prophet: Referring to the Prophet Muhammad, peace be upon him, the last prophet and messenger sent by God to to all of mankind.

11. Sallalahu Alayhi Wa Salam: May Allah's peace and blessings be upon him (the Prophet Muhammad)

◄•‣ Appendix •‣►

Ahadeeth

Sleeping while in a state of Wudu and on your right side
The Messenger of Allah (peace be upon him) said, "When you go to bed, you should perform the ablution (wudu) for the prayer, and then lay down on your right side. Then say, 'O Allah, I have turned my face to You and I have surrendered my self to You and I have committed my back to You out of fear and desire for You. There is no place of safety or refuge from You except with You. I have believed in Your book which You revealed and Your Prophet whom You sent.' If you die that night, you will die in fitra (natural state). And make these the last words you utter.'"

Sahih al-Bukhari, Book of Ablutions (4), Chapter (75) The superiority of a person who sleeps with ablution, #247 Or Sahih al-Bukhari, Book: Invocations (80), Chapter (6) To Sleep with ablution, #6311

It is reported that the Messenger of Allah (peace be upon him) said, "Purify these bodies, and Allah will purify you. There is not a servant who spends his night in a state of purification except that an angel spends the night besides him. And whenever the slave turns over during the night, the angel says: 'O Allah, forgive Your slave, for he went to sleep in a state of purification.'"

[Tabarani, al-Mu`jam al-Kabir]

◄ • Appendix • ►

Bedtime Athkar
Narrated `Ali: Fatima complained about the blisters on her hand because of using a mill-stone. She went to ask the Prophet for a servant, but she did not find him (at home) and had to inform `Aisha of her need. When he came, `Aisha informed him about it. `Ali added: The Prophet (peace be upon him) came to us when we had gone to our beds. When I was going to get up, he said, "Stay in your places," and sat between us, till I felt the coolness of the feet on my chest. The Prophet (peace be upon him) then said, "Shall I not tell you of a thing which is better for you than a servant? When you (both) go to your beds, say 'Allahu Akbar' thirty four times, and 'SubhanAllah' thirty three times, 'Al Humdulillah' thirty three times, for that is better for you than a servant." Ibn Seereen said, "SubhanAllah' (is to be said for) thirty four times."

Sahih al-Bukhari, Book: Invocations (80), Chapter (11) Saying Takbir and Tasbih on going to bed, #6318

Reciting the 3 Qul's
Aisha (may Allah be pleased with her) narrated that when the Prophet (peace be upon him) went to bed every night, he would hold his hands together and blow into them, and recite into them Qul Huwa Allaahu Ahad, Qul a'oodhu bi rabb il-falaq and Qul a'oodhu bi rabb il-naas. Then he would wipe his hands over whatever he could of his body, starting with his head and face and the front of his body, and he would do that three times.

Sahih al-Bukhari, Book: Invocations (80), Chapter (12) Taking refuge with Allah, and the recitation before going to bed, #6319

◄• Appendix •►

Additional Sunnahs for Advanced Children

1. Reciting Ayah al Kursi (Surah al Baqarah, verse 255)
The Prophet (peace be upon him) said, "By reciting it (Ayah al Kursi), there will be a guardian appointed over you from Allah who will protect you during the night, and Satan will not be able to come near you until morning"

Sahih al-Bukhari, Book: Virtues of the Qur'an (66), Chapter (10) The superiority of Surah al Baqarah, #5010 or Sahih al-Bukhari, Book: Representation, Authorization, Business by Proxy (40), Chapter (10) If a person deputes somebody, and the deputy leaves something, #2311

2. Reciting the last two verses of Surah al Baqarah
Abu Mas'ud (May Allah be pleased with him) reported: I heard the Prophet (peace be upon him) saying, "He who recites the two Ayahs at the end of Surah al Baqarah at night, they will suffice him."

Sahih al-Bukhari, Book: Virtues of the Qur'an (66), Chapter (34) What is the proper period for reciting the whole Qur'an, #5051

◄ •• Appendix •• ►

3. The following duas are said before bed and when waking in the morning
Narrated Hudhaifa: When the Prophet (peace be upon him) went to bed, he would say: "Bismika amutu wa ahya." And when he got up he would say: "Al Hamdulillahil-ladhi ahyana ba'da ma amatana wa ilaihin-nushur."

Sahih al-Bukhari, Book: Invocations (80), Chapter (7) What to say if going to bed, #6312, or Sahih al-Bukhari, Book: Invocations (80), Chapter (16) What to say if one gets up in the morning, #6324

Narrated Hudhaifa: Whenever the Prophet (peace be upon him) lay down for sleep at night, he would place his (right) hand under his (right) cheek and supplicate: "Allahumma bismika amutu wa ahya [O Allah, with Your Name will I die and live (wake up)]." And when he woke up, he would supplicate: "Al Hamdulillahil-ladhi ahyana ba'da ma amatana, wa ilaihin-nushur (All praise is due to Allah, Who has brought us back to life after He has caused us to die, and to Him is the return)."

Sahih al-Bukhari, Book: Invocations (80), Chapter (8) Putting your right hand under your right cheek, #6314

Reference: www.sunnah.com

◄ • The Author • ►

Alia G. Dada was born and raised in Southern California. She graduated from Cal Poly Pomona with a Bachelors Degree in Business Administration and a Minor in the Spanish Language. Shortly after, she moved to Cairo, Egypt. After privately studying Arabic she went on to obtain her degree in Islamic Law (Shariah) from the Al-Azhar University. Blessed with a child who has a love for reading, she was inspired to write a book that would help caregivers water the seed of faith and Islamic literacy in the hearts of young Muslims.